THE BEST OF *Larry*

POP-UP BOOKS

MARY ROSE

THE BEST OF
Larry

Foreword by Alan Coren

DAVID & CHARLES
Newton Abbot   London   North Pomfret

Larry and the publishers wish to thank the Editors of *Punch* and *Private Eye* for permission to use material from those magazines.

British Library Cataloguing in Publication Data

Larry
   The best of Larry.
   1. English wit and humour, Pictorial
   I. Title
   741.5′942   NC1479

   ISBN 0-7153-8544-5

Printed in Great Britain
by Redwood Burn Limited, Trowbridge, Wiltshire
for David & Charles (Publishers) Limited
Brunel House   Newton Abbot   Devon

Published in the United States of America
by David & Charles Inc
North Pomfret   Vermont 05053   USA

Foreword

Larry is the only cartoonist I can think of who does not excite the rage of writers.

It may, of course, come as a surprise to civilians outside the grisly perimeter of the comic battlefield that any such discord exists between those humorists who draw and those who type: innocent readers, coming, say, across a magazine like *Punch* and falling about at what they see as the combined and complementary wit of cartoonists and writers, doubtless see the enterprise as one of mutual help and friendship, a bright brotherhood of genius holding court on premises where the only noise is that of men rolling on the floor and laughing helplessly at one another's comic brilliance.

The truth of the matter is that writers and cartoonists hate one another's guts. Cartoonists feel that writers spend a thousand words and take up invaluable space on an idea that can be put across in a ten-word caption under a drawing, and writers grind their teeth at the fact that a cartoonist who knows nothing about words has squandered an idea that could run for profitable pages on a one-line caption.

But Larry is exempt from all this.

Larry does not write. Larry is the quintessential cartoonist, in that his genius—and that is exactly what it is—resides entirely in his extraordinary and astonishing visual breadth and penetration. No-one could write what Larry sees; no-one could invest the mundane and the inanimate with the crazy, surreal, wonderfully hilarious life with which Larry endows the leaden objects of the everyday. With Chaplin and Keaton and Harold Lloyd long gone, Larry is the only great silent comedian still in business.

His active life has been longer than theirs. For thirty years, in thousands and thousands of superlative cartoons, Larry's fertility and inventiveness have never flagged; he has produced a body of work in which the whole of human daftness has been so meticulously and comprehensively delineated that the very word *Larry* seems to many of us to have entered the language: people may be said to be 'straight out of Larry', incidents may be seen as 'Larry situations'. Larry is a brand that identifies more than itself: he is at one with Hoover and Biro and Thermos.

And, to those of us who see the world as a spot much in need of laughter, he is more necessary than any of them.

Alan Coren

Christmas Party

THIS EXPERIENCE MAY BE UNSUITABLE FOR PEOPLE OF A NERVOUS DISPOSITION

JACQUES COUSTEAU

TUSSAUDS WAXWORKS

Punks on Holiday

RODIN'S 'DRUNK'

SOAP RECOVERY SHIP

Plumbers

Empties
(Post~Budget Pubs)

Car Workers

MODEL VILLAGE

VISITORS BOOK

RODIN'S
HOT
BATH-WATER

Firemen

"DAD'S HOME!"

Grave
Situations
for Cricketers

Works Pantomime

Man in Apron

1.

2

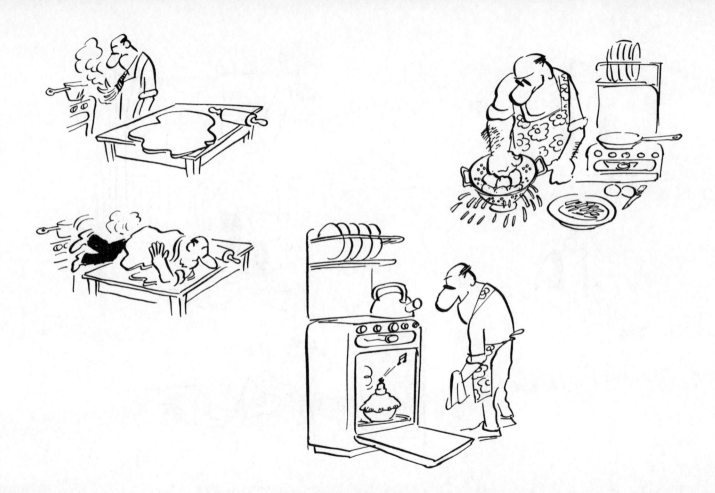

Man in School

Homelea Hotel

Butchers

Wallpapering

More Man in School

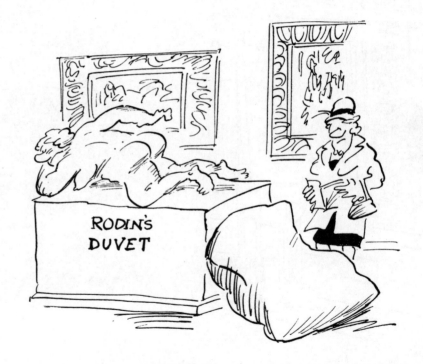

More Man in Apron

Flying Doctor

CAMPAIGN
FOR REAL
SPIT'N
SAWDUST

PARADE
OF
BOATS
2-30

AFTER & SEX
MINTS

Victorian Rush Hour

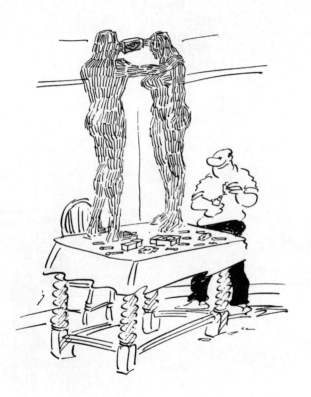

More **Butchers**

Haunted Pubs

RODIN'S
SOFT
PORNOGRAPHER

YOUR
SILHOUETTE
IN A
JIFFY

MEN
BAND

Punkerella

Home for the Holidays